A BOOK OF
SCOTTISH NURSERY RHYMES

A BOOK OF
Scottish Nursery Rhymes

Collected and edited by
NORAH & WILLIAM
MONTGOMERIE

✳

Illustrated by T. RITCHIE
and N. MONTGOMERIE

New York
OXFORD UNIVERSITY PRESS
1965

© The Hogarth Press 1964

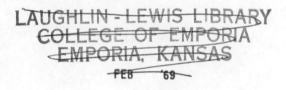
'75.9 -1042

Library of Congress Catalogue Card Number: 65-14598

PRINTED IN THE UNITED STATES OF AMERICA

TO OUR GRANDCHILDREN
AND
THEIR GRANDCHILDREN

INTRODUCTION

SINCE our two collections of Scottish Nursery Rhymes were published in the first years of the post-war welfare state, the tide of the Scottish language, in which they were born, has ebbed further and left these seashells lying higher up the beach. But, like the sea urchins we picked up then on a Scottish shore and still look at with pleasure, they have lost none of their fascination.

It should not be necessary to point out that a language is learned, and a culture planted, in childhood. So these rhymes should precede the pleasure derived from hearing the more mature Scottish ballads and folksongs. Indeed the fundamental quality of these rhymes attunes the young ear to all poetry.

Because we were then more politically aware of their connection with a national language somewhat different from English, we made the spelling of these rhymes as Scottish as we could, to preserve the full flavour. So now, noticing the gap between these verses and the culture that gave them birth, we have reversed the process of preservation by spelling them as near as possible to the common language of these islands without destroying the essential differences which are, in a sense, the artistic style of their creators. Like Burns, we trust the reader to read these Scottish rhymes in broad Scots—if he knows broad Scots.

Even as we write this, "Johnnie Tod has taen a notion" comes over the radio sung by a lively group of popular young folksingers. This reminds us that these rhymes are not unconnected with the current revival of folksong on both sides of the Atlantic.

NORAH AND WILLIAM MONTGOMERIE

Broughty Ferry
November 1963

CONTENTS

9

13

SOME WORDS YOU MAY
NOT KNOW

ahin, behind
ava, at all

bannock, cake
bawbee, halfpenny
ben, in the front room
bide, tarry
big, build
braw, brave
bree, water in which food is
    boiled
brod, brad, nail
Broomielaw, hill of broom
    (near River Clyde, Glas-
    gow)
brosy, stout, well-fed
busk, dress
but, (in the) kitchen

carse, stretch of flat, fertile
    land near river
caw, drive
chafts, jaws, cheeks
chap, knock at door
chappit tatties, mashed potatoes
clap, pat
clocking, *clucking*, hatching
coble, small boat
coft, bought
coll, haycock
collop, portion
corbie, crow
crowping, croaking
cruppen, crept

cutty, short

die, toy

fa, who
fluke, duck's bill
Fozlin Een, weak eyes

gaddie, gaudy
gait, road
gar cast her a pickle, go, throw
    her a little food
gin, if
gled, kite
goldspink, goldfinch
greetie, weeping
grice, young pig

hantle, a large number
hap and row, wrap up
hirple, limp
Hogmanay, last day of year
hollin, holly
hoolie, softly
hotch, heave
hummel, hornless
hurcheon, hedgehog

jimp, slender

ken, know
kisty, chest
kitchen, cooked meat
knowe, hillock

16

lift, sky
luckenbooth, booth made to be locked up
lug, ear

maun, must
mickle, *muckle*, big
minnie, mother
morn (the), to-morrow
moss, peat bog
mouter, miller's fee
muir, moor

neb, beak, nose

oxter, armpit

papingoe, parrot
puddock, frog, toad
pyat, magpie

roperee, rope-walk
rotten, rat
roupie, hoarse

shathmont, span
sic, such
siccar, sure
sneck, door-latch
soop, sweep
soople Tam, top

soutar, cobbler
sowdie, hodge-podge
spelder, stretch out the legs
spier, enquire
steer, stir, move
stock, butcher's table
studdy, anvil
syboes, spring onions
syne, then

tirl at the pin, attract attention at the door
titlin, meadow-pippit or titlark
theevil, stick for stirring
thimber, massive
thrum, loose end
trig, neat

unco, very

wame, belly
wapenshaw, show of arms
what way? Why?
whiles, sometimes
windy sole, window sill
winnock, window
wonne, dwelling

yestreen, last night

ANE! Twa! Three!
Ane! Twa! Three!
Sic a lot o fisher-wifies
I do see!

Auchmithie

1

"PUSSY, pussy baudrons,
Where have you been?"
"I've been to London,
To see the Queen!"

Pussy, pussy baudrons,
What got you there?"
"I got a good fat mousikie,
Running up a stair!"

"Pussy, pussy baudrons,
What did you do with it?"
"I put it in my meal-poke
To eat to my bread!"

2

MOUSIE, mousie, come to me,
The cat's awa frae hame,
Mousie, mousie come to me,
I'll use you kind and make you tame.

3

THE cattie rade to Paisley, to Paisley, to Paisley,
The cattie rade to Paisley upon a harrow tine;
And she came louping hame again,
And she came louping hame again,
And she came louping hame again
Upon a mare o mine.
It was upon a Wednesday,
A windy, windy Wednesday,
It was upon a Wednesday,
Gin I can rightly mind.

4

THE Robin came to the Wren's nest,
And keekit in, and keekit in,
"O wae's me on your old pow,
Would you be in, would you be in?
For you shall never lie without,
And me within, and me within,
As lang as I have an old clout,
To row you in, to row you in."

5

THERE was a wee bit mousikie,
That lived in Gilberaty, O;
It couldna get a bite o cheese,
For cheetie-pussy-cattie, O.

I said unto the cheesikie,
"O fain would I be at you, O,
If it werena for the cruel paws
Of cheetie-pussy-cattie, O."

6

TAMMY, Tammy Titmouse,
Lay an egg in ilka house,
Ane for you, and ane for me,
And ane for Tammy Titmouse.
Edinburgh

7

THE doggies gaed to the mill,
This way and that way,
They took a lick out of this wife's poke,
They took a lick out of that wife's poke,
And a loup in the laid and a dip in the dam,
And gaed walloping, walloping, walloping hame.

8

WEE chookie birdie,
Toll -oll -oll,
Laid an egg
On the windy sole.

The windy sole
Began to crack;
  Wee chookie birdie
  Roared and grat.
          Glasgow

9

Go, go, go,
Go to Berwick, Johnnie.
You shall have the horse,
I shall have the pony.

10

Trot, trot, horsie,
Going awa to Fife,
Coming back on Monday,
With a new wife.

11

THE black and the brown
Gang nearest the town,
John Paterson's filly gaes foremost.

The black and the grey
Gang all their ain way,
John Paterson's filly gaes foremost.

The black and the dun
They fell all ahin,
John Paterson's filly gaes foremost.

The black and the yellow
Gae up like a swallow,
John Paterson's filly gaes foremost.

Ayrshire

12

I HAD a little hobby-horse,
His mane was dapple grey;
His head was made of pease-straw,
His tail was made of hay.

13

I HAD a wee cock and I loved it well,
I fed my cock on yonder hill;
   My cock, lily-cock, lily-cock, coo,
   Every one loves their cock, why should I not love
      my cock too?

I had a wee hen, and I loved it well,
I fed my hen on yonder hill,

My hen, chuckie, chuckie,
My cock, lily-cock, lily-cock, coo,
Every one loves their cock, why should I not love
    my cock too?

I had a wee duck, and I loved it well,
I fed my duck on yonder hill,
    My duck, wheetie, wheetie,
    My hen, chuckie, chuckie,
    My cock, lily-cock, lily-cock, coo.
    Every one loves their cock, why should I not love
        my cock too?

I had a wee sheep, and I loved it well,
I fed my sheep on yonder hill,
    My sheep, maie, maie,
    My duck, wheetie, wheetie,
    My hen, chuckie, chuckie,
    My cock, lily-cock, lily-cock, coo.
    Every one loves their cock, why should I not love
        my cock too?

I had a wee dog, and I loved it well,
I fed my dog on yonder hill,
    My dog, bouffie, bouffie,
    My sheep, maie, maie,
    My duck, wheetie, wheetie,
    My hen chuckie, chuckie,
    My cock, lily-cock, lily-cock, coo,
    Every one loves their cock, why should I not love
        my cock too?

I had a wee cat, and I loved her well,
I fed my cat on yonder hill,
   My cat cheetie, cheetie,
   My dog, bouffie, bouffie,
   My sheep, maie, maie,
   My duck, wheetie, wheetie,
   My hen, chuckie, chuckie,
   My cock, lily-cock, lily-cock, coo,
   Every one loves their cock, why should I not love
      my cock too?

I had a wee pig, and I loved it well,
I fed my pig on yonder hill,
   My pig, squeakie, squeakie,
   My cat cheetie, cheetie,
   My dog, bouffie, bouffie,
   My sheep, maie, maie,
   My duck, wheetie, wheetie,
   My hen, chuckie, chuckie,
   My cock, lily-cock, lily-cock, coo,
   Every one loves their cock, why should I not love
      my cock too?

14

WREN AND DOVE

THE wee Coorie Anne
Can lay twenty-one,
But the big Cushie Doo
Can only lay two.

15

LADYBIRD

LADY, Lady Landers,
Lady, Lady Landers,
Take up your cloak
About your head,

And fly away
To Flanders.
Fly o'er firth,
And fly o'er fell,
Fly o'er pool,
And running well,
Fly o'er moor,
And fly o'er mead,
Fly o'er living,
Fly o'er dead,
Fly o'er corn,
And fly o'er lea,
Fly o'er river,
Fly o'er sea,
Fly you east,
Or fly you west,
Fly to him
That loves me best.

16

THE HUNTING OF THE WREN

WILL you go to the wood? quo Fozie Mozie;
Will you go to the wood? quo Johnie Rednosie;
Will you go to the wood? quo Fozlin Ene;
Will you go to the wood? quo brother and kin.

What to do there? quo Fozie Mozie;
What to do there? quo Johnie Rednosie;
What to do there? quo Fozlin Ene;
What to do there? quo brother and kin.

To slay the Wren, quo Fozie Mozie;
To slay the Wren, quo Johnie Rednosie;
To slay the Wren, quo Fozlin Ene;
To slay the Wren, quo brother and kin.

What way will you get her hame? quo Fozie Mozie;
What way will you get her hame? quo Johnie Rednosie;
What way will you get her hame? quo Fozlin Ene;
What way will you get her hame? quo brother and kin.

We'll hire cart and horse, quo Fozie Mozie;
We'll hire cart and horse, quo Johnie Rednosie;
We'll hire cart and horse, quo Fozlin Ene;
We'll hire cart and horse, quo brother and kin.

What way will you get her in? quo Fozie Mozie;
What way will you get her in? quo Johnie Rednosie;
What way will you get her in? quo Fozlin Ene;
What way will you get her in? quo brother and kin.

We'll drive down the door-cheeks, quo Fozie Mozie;
We'll drive down the door-cheeks, quo Johnie Rednosie;
We'll drive down the door-cheeks, quo Fozlin Ene;
We'll drive down the door-cheeks, quo brother and kin.

I'll have a wing, quo Fozie Mozie;
I'll have another, quo Johnie Rednosie;
I'll have a leg, quo Fozlin Ene;
And I'll have another, quo brother and kin.

17

THE bonnie moor-hen
Has feathers enou
The bonnie moor-hen
Has feathers enou.

There's some of them black,
And there's some of them blue,
The bonnie moor-hen
Has feathers enou.

18

THE cuckoo's a bonnie bird,
He sings as he flies;
He brings us good tidings,
He tells us nae lies.

He drinks the cold water,
To keep his voice clear;
And he'll come again
In the spring of the year.

19

THERE were two crows sat on a stone,
　　　Fal de ral,
One flew away and there remained one,
　　　Fal de ral,
The other seeing his neighbour gone,
　　　Fal de ral,
He flew away and there was none,
　　　Fal de ral.

20

ROON, roon, rosie,
Cuppie, cuppie, shell,
The dog's away to Hamilton
To buy a new bell;
If you don't take it
I'll take it to myself.
Roon, roon, rosie,
Cuppie, cuppie, shell.

21

COCK AND HEN

ILKA day,
An egg I lay,
And yet I aye go barefoot,
Barefoot.

I've been through all the town,
Seeking you a pair of shoon;
Would you have my heart out,
Heart out?

22

THE silly bit chicken!
Gar cast her a pickle,
And she'll grow mickle,
And she'll grow mickle.

And she'll grow mickle,
And she'll do good,
And lay an egg
To my little brood.

23

HIS father died
And left him a horse,
A bonny little horse
That gaed trot, trot, trot!

Wing, wing waddelery,
Jake sing saddelery,
Little boy waddelery
Under the brow!

He sellt the horse,
And he bought a cow,
A bonny little cow
That said, "Moo, moo, moo!"

He sellt the cow,
And he bought a sow,
A bonny little sow
That said, "Grumph, grumph, grumph!"
Glasgow

24

MADAM Pussie's coming hame,
Riding on a grey stane.
What's to the supper?
Pease brose and butter.

Who'll say the grace?
I'll say the grace.
Leviticus, Levaticus,
Taste, taste, taste!

25

I HAD a little pony,
They called it Dapple Grey;
I lent it to a lady,
To ride a mile away.

She whipped it, she lashed it,
She drove it o'er the brae;
I willna lend my pony more,
Gin all the ladies pay.

26

"JOHN SMITH, fellow fine,
Can you shoe this horse of mine?"
"Aye, sir, and that I can,
As well as ony man!
There's a nail upon the tae,
To make the pony climb the brae,
There's the nail upon the heel,
To help the pony pace well;
There's a nail, and there's a brod,
There's a horsie well shod."

27

CAW Hawkie, drive Hawkie,
Caw Hawkie through the water.

Hawkie is a good milk cow,
But Hawkie will not wade the water.

I'll cast off my hose and shoon,
And I'll drive Hawkie through the water.

28

WASH well the fresh fish, wash well the fresh fish,
Wash well the fresh fish,
   And skim well the bree;
For there's many a foul-footed thing, many a foul-footed
  thing,
Many a foul-footed thing
   In the salt sea.

I'll catch the white fish, I'll catch the white fish
I'll catch the white fish
   To please my lassie's ee;
But the bonny black-backit fish, the bonny black-backit
  fish,
The bonny black-backit fish
   Has aye the sweetest bree.

BONNIE lady,
Let down your milk,
And I'll give you
A gown of silk,
A gown of silk,
And a ball of twine,
Bonnie lady,
Your milk's not mine.

Clydesdale

SING, sing!
What shall I sing?
The cat ran awa
With my apron string.

Galloway

31

HERE'S a string of wild geese,
How many for a penny?
One to my lord,
And one to my lady;
Up the gait and down the gait;
They're all flown from me.

32

ON the first of March,
The craws begin to search;
By the first of April,
They are sitting still;
By the first of May,
They're all flown away;
Crowping greedy back again,
With October's wind and rain.

33

SKYLARK

UP in the lift go we,
Te-hee, te-hee, te-hee!
There's not a soutar on the earth
Can make a shoe to me, to me!
Why so, why so, why so?
Because my heel's as lang as my toe.

THE RAVEN AND THE CROW

THE corbie with his roupie throat
Cried frae the leafless tree,
"Come o'er the loch, come o'er the loch,
Come o'er the loch wi me!"

The craw put out his sooty head,
And cried, "Whaur tae, whaur tae?"
"To yonder field," the corbie cried,
"Where there is corn enow.

"The ploughman ploughed the land yestreen,
The farmer sowed this morn,
And we can mak a full fat meal,
From off the broadcast corn."

The twa black birds flew o'er the trees,
They flew towards the sun;
The farmer watching by the hedge
Shot baith with his lang gun.

ROBIN, Robin Redbreast,
Cutty, cutty wran,
Gin you harry my nest,
You'll never be a man.

36

ROBIN, Robin Redbreast
Sits upon a rail;
He nods with his head,
And wags with his tail.

37

EARWIG

THE horny goloch is an awesome beast,
Supple and scaly;
It has twa horns, and a hantle of feet,
And a forkie tailie.

38

CHEESE and bread
For the bat, bat, bat;
Come into
My hat, hat, hat.

39

THE lion and the unicorn
Fighting for the crown;
Up jumped the wee dog,
And knocked them both down.

Some got white bread,
And some got brown,
But the lion beat the unicorn,
Round about the town.

40

THE grey cat's kittled in Charlie's wig,
The grey cat's kittled in Charlie's wig;
There's one of them living and two of them dead,
The grey cat's kittled in Charlie's wig.

41

LINGLE, lingle, lang tang,
Our cat's dead!
What did she die with?
With a sore head!

All you that kent her,
When she was alive,
Come to her burial,
Atween four and five.

42

CURLEW

Wheepy whaupy,
Wheepy, whaupy,
Wheepy whaupy,
Wife o the glen!
Will you no waken,
Waken, waken,
Will you no waken,
Wife o the glen?

The men of the lowlands
Are stealing your cattle,
They're stealing your cattle,
And killing your men.
Wheepy whaupy,
Wheepy whaupy,
Wheepy whaupy,
Wife o the glen!

43

A wee bird sat upon a tree,
When the year was done and auld,
And aye it cheepit sae pitiously,
"My, but it's cald, cald!"

FACE GAME

CHAP at the door,
Keek in,
Lift the sneck,
    Walk in.

WHAT'S in there?
Gold and money.
Where's my share o't?
The mousie ran awa wi't.
Where's the mousie?
In her housie.
Where's her housie?
In the wood.
Where's the wood?
The fire burnt it.
Where's the fire?
The water quenched it.
Where's the water?
The brown bull drank it.
Where's the brown bull?
Back of Burnie's Hill.
Where's Burnie's Hill?
All clad with snow.
Where's the snow?
The sun melted it.
Where's the sun?
High, high up in the air.

46

THUMB AND FINGER GAME

THIS is the man that broke the barn,
This is the man that stealt the corn,
This is the man that ran awa,
This is the man that telt all,
And poor Pirlie-winkie paid for all, paid for all.

47

TICKLING GAME

ADAM and Eve gaed up my sleeve,
To fetch me down some candy.

Adam and Eve came down my sleeve,
And said there was none till Monday.

48

FINGER GAME

TWO wee birdies,
Sitting on a hill,
One called Jack,
And the other called Jill.
Flee away Jack!
Flee away Jill!
Come back Jack!
Come back Jill!

49

THIS is the way the ladies ride,
Jimp and small, jimp and small,
This is the way the gentlemen ride,
Trotting all, trotting all,
This is the way the cadgers ride,
Creels and all, creels and all!

50

TICKLING GAME

THERE was a wee mouse
And he had a wee house,
And he lived in there.

And he gaed creepy-crappy,
Creep-crappy,
And made a wee hole in there.

51

HEY my kitten, my kitten,
Hey my kitten, my dearie,
Sic a foot as this
Was na far nor nearie.
Here we go up, up, up,
Here we go down, down, downie;
Here we go back and fore;
Here we go round and roundie;
Here's a leg for a stocking
And here's a foot for a shoe-ie!

52

I HAD a little manikin, I set him on my thumbikin;
I saddled him, I bridled him, and sent him to the
     townikin;
I bought a pair of garters to tie his wee bit hosikin;
I bought a pocket handkerchief to dight his wee bit
     nosikin;
I sent him in the garden to fetch a pound of sage,
And found him in the kitchen nook kissing little Madge.

53

BROW, brow, brenty,
Eye, eye, winkie,
Nose, nose, nebbie,
Cheek, cheek, cherry,
Mou, mou, merry,
Chin, chin, chackie,
Catch a fly, catch a fly!

54

TICKLING GAME

THERE was a man
In Muir of Skene,
He had dirks
And I had none;
But I fell on him
With my thumbs,
And wot you how
I dirkit him,
Dirkit him,
Dirkit him?

55

HICKETY, bickety, pease scone,
Where shall this poor Scotsman go?
Will he go east, will he go west,
Or will he go to the crow's nest?

56

SKIPPING

THE wind and the wind and the wind blows high,
The rain comes scattering from the sky;
Margaret Morrison says she'll die
For the lad with the roving eye.

She is handsome, she is pretty,
She is the girl of the golden city;
She has lovers, one, two, three,
Pray tell me who they'll be.

David Thomson says he loves her,
All the boys a fighting for her;
Let them all say what they will,
David Thomson has her still.

Lead her by the lily-white hand,
Lead her by the water;
Give her kisses, one, two, three,
For Mrs. Morrison's daughter.

Lundy

57

Ring a ring a pinkie
Ring a ring a bell,
If I break the bargain,
I'll go to Hell.

58

Hiccup, hiccup,
Go away,
Come again
Another day!

Hiccup, hiccup,
When I bake,
I'll give you
A butter cake!

59

SKIPPING

Down in the valley
  Where the green grass grows,
Jessy Thomson
  Hanging out her clothes.

She sang and she sang,
  And she sang so sweet,
Till she saw Billy
  Coming down the street.

Billy Blain,
  Will you marry me?
Yes dear, yes love,
  At half-past three.

I've cut cake and spiced cake,
  And ham, for tea,
All for the wedding
  Of you and me.

51

COUNTING OUT

I SAW a dove
Fly o'er the dam
With silver wings
And golden band.

She lookit east,
She lookit west,
She lookit where
To light on best.

She lighted on
A bank of sand,
To see the cocks
Of Cumberland.

White pudding,
Black trout,
You're out!

61

HERE is a lass with a golden ring,
Golden ring, golden ring,
Here is a lass with a golden ring,
So early in the morning.

Gentle Johnnie kissed her,
Three times blessed her,
Sent her a slice of bread and butter
In a silver saucer.

62

A DIS, a dis, a green grass,
A dis, a dis, a dis,
Come all you bonnie lassies,
And dance along with us.

For we shall go a-roving,
A-roving in the land;
We'll take this bonnie lassie,
We'll take her by the hand.

And you shall have a duck, my dear,
And you shall have a drake;
And you shall have a young prince,
A young prince for your mate.

63

I've a kisty,
I've a creel,
I've a baggie
Full of meal.

I've a doggie
At the door,
One, two,
Three, four.

64

A PIN to see the puppet show,
A pin to see a die,
A pin to see an old man
Climbing to the sky.

HERE we go round the jing-a-ring,
Jing-a-ring, jing-a-ring;
Here we go round the jing-a-ring,
About the merry-matanzie.

Twice about, and then we fall,
Then we fall, then we fall,
Twice about and then we fall,
About the merry-matanzie.

Guess you who the goodman is,
Goodman is, goodman is,
Guess you who the goodman is,
About the merry matanzie.

Honey is sweet, and so is he,
So is he, so is he,
Honey is sweet and so is he,
About the merry-matanzie.

He's married with a gay gold ring,
A gay gold ring, a gay gold ring;
He's married with a gay gold ring,
About the merry-matanzie.

Now they're married, we'll wish them joy,
Wish them joy, wish them joy;
Now they're married we'll wish them joy,
About the merry-matanzie.

Father and mother they must obey,
Must obey, must obey,
Father and mother they must obey,
About the merry-matanzie.

Loving each other like brother and sister,
Sister and brother, sister and brother,
Loving each other like sister and brother,
About the merry-matanzie.

We pray the couple to kiss together,
Kiss together, kiss together,
We pray the couple to kiss together,
About the merry-matanzie.

66

I'LL give you a pin to stick in your thumb,
To carry a lady to London town.

London town's a very braw place,
All covered o'er with gold and lace.

Hotch her up, and hotch her down,
Hotch her into London town.

67

YOUR plack and my plack,
Your plack and my plack,
Your plack and my plack,
And Jennie's bawbee.

We'll put them in the pint stoup,
Pint stoup, pint stoup,
We'll put them in the pint stoup,
And join all three.

And that was all my Jenny had,
My Jenny had, my Jenny had,
And all that my Jenny had,
Was a bawbee.

SINGING GAME

THIS is a boy's game. One boy stands with his back to a
wall. A second bends towards him so that his back is a
table. One by one the other boys advance and hammer on
the "table's" back with their fists, for the duration of a
verse and the "table's" endurance, singing:

> And it's baking, Bessy Bell,
>   Come a ree, O, come a raddie, O;
> And it's baking, Bessy Bell,
>   Come a ree, O, come a raddie, O.

> And it's on with the hammer and the block,
>   Come a ree, O, come a raddie, O;
> And it's on with the hammer and the block,
>   Come a ree, O, come a raddie, O.

> And it's on with the studdy and the stock,
>   Come a ree, O, come a raddie, O;
> And it's on with the studdy and the stock,
>   Come a ree, O, come a raddie, O.

> Then it's on with the kettle and the pan,
>   Come a ree, O, come a raddie, O;
> Then it's on with the kettle and the pan,
>   Come a ree, O, come a raddie, O.

Then it's on with the poker and the tongs,
 Come a ree, O, come a raddie, O;
Then it's on with the poker and the tongs,
 Come a ree, O, come a raddie, O.

Then it's on with the watering can,
 Come a ree, O, come a raddie, O;
Then it's on with the watering can,
 Come a ree, O, come a raddie, O.

And it's on with the red cowl man,
 Come a ree, O, come a raddie, O;
And it's on with the red cowl man,
 Come a ree, O, come a raddie, O.

69

O, THE mill, mill, O!
And the kiln, kiln, O!
And the cogging of Peggy's wheel, O!
The sack and the sieve,
And all she did leave,
To dance the Miller's reel, O!

Oʜ, what is Jeannie weeping for,
A-weeping for, a-weeping for,
Oh, what is Jeannie weeping for,
All on a summer's day?

I'm weeping for my own true love,
My own true love, my own true love,
I'm weeping for my own true love,
All on a summer's day.

Rise up and choose another love,
Another love, another love,
Rise up and choose another love,
All on a summer's day.

SINGING GAME

THE children form a line. One of them is chosen to go in front and to walk backward and forward, singing:

> Roses up and roses down,
>   And roses in the garden;
> I would na gie a bunch of roses
>   For twopence ha'penny farden.

She points to a child in the line and sings, naming her:

> Mary Wilson, fresh and fair,
>   A bunch of roses she shall wear,
> Gold and silver by her side;
>   I know who is her bride.

The two girls take hands and go round the line, singing:

> Take her by the lily-white hand,
>   And lead her o'er the water,
> And give her kisses—One! Two! Three!
>   For she's the princess's daughter.

72

WATER, water, wall-flower, growing up so high,
We are all maidens, and we must all die,
Excepting Jeannie Robertson, the youngest of us all,
She can dance and she can sing,
And she can knock us all down.

Fie, fie, fie, for shame,
Turn your back to the wall again.

SINGING GAME

THE players join hands and stand in a line, while one child advances and retreats before them, singing:

> One o'clock, the gun went off,
>> And I can stay no longer.
> If I do, Mama will say
>> I play with the boys up yonder.
>
> My stockings red, my garters blue,
>> My boots all bound with silver;
> A red, red rose upon my breast
>> And a gold ring on my finger.

She chooses a player from the line and they birl round together, singing:

> Heigh-ho, for Annie O!
>> My bonnie, bonnie Annie O!
> If I had but one to choose
>> I'd choose my bonnie Annie O!

The first girl then joins the line, leaving the other to advance and retreat before it as the game is repeated.

74

SKIPPING

EVIE-OVIE,
Turn the rope over;
Mother in the market,
Selling penny baskets;
Baby in the cradle,
Playing with a ladle.

75

BOBBIE SHAFTOE'S gone to sea,
Silver buckles on his knee,
He'll come home and marry me,
Bonnie Bobbie Shaftoe.

Bobbie Shaftoe's fat and fair,
Combing down his yellow hair;
He's my love for evermair,
Bonnie Bobbie Shaftoe.

SINGING GAME

THE children, all except one, stand in a row. This one is Gentle Robin, and stands a short distance in front of the others. The children in the row sing:

> Here comes Gentle Robin,
>   With sugar cakes and wine;
> Here comes Gentle Robin,
>   With sugar cakes and wine.

Robin sings:

> O ladies, will you taste it,
>   Taste it, taste it?
> O ladies, will you taste it,
>   Before you go away?

Gentle Robin walks round the row, singing:

> We'll first go round the kitchen,
>   The kitchen, the kitchen;
> We'll first go round the kitchen,
>   And then go round the hall.

The row of children answers:

> Come, choose you out the fairest,
>   The fairest, the fairest;
> Come, choose you out the fairest,
>   The fairest of them all.

Gentle Robin takes one girl by the hand, and sings:

> The fairest one that I can see
> Is pretty Mary. Come with me!
> The fairest one that I can see
> Is pretty Mary. Come with me!

Gentle Robin leads Mary out. They clasp each other, and whirl round, while everybody sings:

> And now we've got a beautiful maid
> To join us in our dancing.
> Come ransome dansum, jolly me jump,
> Come a ransum dansum day.

Gentle Robin returns to the row, and his partner becomes Gentle Robin The game begins again.

77

> GREEN peas, mutton pies,
> Tell me where my Jeannie lies,
> And I'll be with her ere she rise,
> And cuddle her to my bosom.
>
> I love Jeannie over and over,
> I love Jeannie among the clover;
> I love Jeannie, and Jeannie loves me,
> That's the lass that I'll go wi.

SINGING GAME

The children form a circle and dance round singing:

Cam you by the salmon fishers?
  Cam you by the roperee?
Saw you a sailor laddie
  Waiting on the coast for me?

I ken far I'm gaeing,
  I ken fa's gaeing wi me;
I hae a lad o my ain,
  You daurna tak him frae me.

Stocking of blue silk,
  Shoes of patent leather,
Kid to tie them up,
  And gold rings on his finger.

O for six o'clock!
  O for seven I weary!
O for eight o'clock!
  And then I'll see my dearie.

Aberdeenshire

79

SINGING GAME

CHILDREN join hands in a ring and raise their arms to make arches. One child then runs in and out of the arches, singing:

> In and out the dusty bluebells,
> In and out the dusty bluebells,
> In and out the dusty bluebells,
>   I am the master.

She taps the shoulder of one of the children, singing:

> Tippety, tappety, on your shoulder,
> Tippety, tappety, on your shoulder,
> Tippety, tappety, on your shoulder,
>   I am the master.

The song begins again, both children going round, one following the other. The game is repeated till only one child is left from the ring. This child begins the game again.

80

> TIP and toe,
> Leemon lo,
> Turn the ship,
> And away we go.

81

How many miles to Glasgow Lea?
Sixty, seventy, eighty-three.

Will I be there by candle light?
Just if your legs be long and tight.

Open your gates and let me through!
Not without a beck and a bow.

There's your beck and there's your bow,
Open your gates and let me through!

82

DAB a pin in my lottery book,
Dab one, dab twa,
Dab all your pins awa!

83

SINGING GAME

JOINING hands, the children form a ring round the
Farmer, and dance round singing:

> The Farmer in his den,
> The Farmer in his den;
> Hey O, me daddy O,
> The Farmer in his den.

> The Farmer takes a Wife,
> The Farmer takes a Wife;
> Hey O, me daddy O.
> The Farmer takes a Wife.

The Farmer in the centre now chooses a wife from the
ring. She joins him in the middle, and the ring dances
round again, singing:

> The Wife takes a Child,
> The Wife takes a Child;
> Hey O, me daddy O,
> The Wife takes a Child.

The Wife chooses a Child from the ring. The Child
joins the two in the middle, and the ring continues:

> The Child takes a Nurse,
> The Child takes a Nurse;
> Hey O, me daddy O,
> The Child takes a Nurse.

The Child chooses a Nurse from the ring. The Nurse joins the three in the middle, and the ring continues:

> The Nurse takes a Dog,
> The Nurse takes a Dog;
>   Hey O, me daddy O,
> The Nurse takes a Dog.

The Nurse chooses a Dog from the ring. The Dog joins the four in the middle, and the ring continues:

> The Dog stands still,
> The Dog stands still;
>   Hey O, me daddy O,
> The Dog stands still.

The ring breaks up, and all the children pat the Dog, singing:
> We all clap the Dog,
> We all clap the Dog;
>   Hey O, me daddy O,
> We all clap the Dog.

The Dog now becomes the Farmer, and the game is repeated.

84

SINGING GAME

JOINING hands, the children make a ring round one
child. They walk round her singing:

> Oats and beans and barley grows,
> Oats and beans and barley grows,
> But you nor I nor nobody knows
> How oats and beans and barley grows.

Standing still and suiting the actions to the words,
they sing:

> First the farmer sows his seeds,
> Then he stands and takes his ease,
> Stamps his feet and clasps his hands,
> Then turns around to view his lands,

each child turning around once. They clasp hands again,
walking round the child in the centre, singing:

> Waiting for a partner,
> Waiting for a partner.
> Open the ring and take one in,

which is the cue for the child in the centre to choose a
partner,

> And kiss her in the centre.

They circle round the couple in the centre, singing:

> Now you're married, you must obey,
> Must be true to all you say;
> You must be kind, you must be good,
> And help your wife to chop the wood.

The child who was first in the centre now joins the
ring, and the game repeats.

85

HERE'S a poor widow from Sandisland,
With all her children by the hand.
One can bake and one can brew,
One can knit and one can sew,
One can sit by the fire and spin,
Another can bake a cake for a King.

Come choose the east,
Come choose the west,
Come choose the one
That you love best.

I choose the fairest one I see,
Catherine Mary come to me.
Now they're married we'll wish them joy,
Every year a girl or boy;
Loving each other like sister and brother,
We pray the couple to kiss together.

86

EIGHT o'clock bells are ringing,
Mother let me out;
My sweetheart is waiting
For to take me out.

He's going to give me apples,
He's going to give me pears,
He's going to give me sixpence,
And kisses on the stairs.

87

THE Quaker's wife sat down to bake,
With all her bairns about her;
She baked them every one a cake,
And the miller wants his mouter.

Sugar and spice and all things nice,
And all things very good in it;
And then the miller sat down to play
A tune upon the spinet.

Merrily danced the Quaker's wife,
And merrily danced the Quaker;
Merrily danced the Quaker's wife,
And merrily danced the Quaker.

"I'LL gie you a pennyworth o preens—
That's aye the way that love begins—
If you'll walk wi me, lady, lady,
If you'll walk wi me, lady."

"I'll no hae your pennyworth o preens—
That's no the way that love begins—
And I'll no walk wi you, wi you,
And I'll no walk wi you."

"O Johnie, O Johnie, what can the matter be,
That I loe this lady, and she loes na me?
And for her sake I maun die, maun die,
And for her sake I maun die!

"I'll gie you a bonny siller box,
Wi seven siller hinges, and seven siller locks,
If you'll walk wi me, lady, lady,
If you'll walk wi me, lady."

"I'll no hae your bonny siller box,
Wi seven siller hinges, and seven siller locks,
And I'll no walk wi you, wi you,
And I'll no walk wi you."

"O Johnie, O Johnie, what can the matter be,
That I loe this lady, and she loes na me?
And for her sake I maun die, maun die,
And for her sake I maun die!

"But I'll gie you a bonnier siller box,
Wi seven gowden hinges and seven gowden locks,
If you'll walk wi me, lady, lady,
If you'll walk wi me, lady."

"I'll no hae your bonnier siller box,
Wi seven gowden hinges, and seven gowden locks,
And I'll no walk wi you, wi you,
And I'll no walk wi you."

"O Johnie, O Johnie, what can the matter be,
That I loe this lady, and she loes na me?
And for her sake I maun die, maun die,
And for her sake I maun die!

"I'll gie you a pair o bonny shoon,
The tane made in Sodom, the tither in Rome,
If you'll walk wi me, lady, lady,
If you'll walk wi me, lady."

"I'll no hae your pair o bonny shoon,
The tane made in Sodom, the tither in Rome,
And I'll no walk wi you, wi you,
And I'll no walk wi you."

"O Johnie, O Johnie, what can the matter be,
That I loe this lady, and she loes na me?
And for her sake I maun die, maun die,
And for her sake I maun die!

I'll gie you the half o Bristol town,
Wi coaches rolling up and down,
If you'll walk wi me, lady, lady,
If you'll walk wi me, lady."

"I'll no hae the half o Bristol town,
Wi coaches rolling up and down,
And I'll no walk wi you, wi you,
And I'll no walk wi you."

"O Johnie, O Johnie, what can the matter be,
That I loe this lady, and she loes na me?
And for her sake I maun die, maun die,
And for her sake I maun die!

"I'll gie you the hale o Bristol town,
Wi coaches rolling up and down,
If you'll walk wi me, lady, lady,
If you'll walk wi me, lady."

"If you'll gie me the hale o Bristol town,
Wi coaches rolling up and down,
I will walk wi you, wi you,
And I will walk wi you."

89

W ᴏ learned you to dance,
Babbity-Bowster, Babbity-Bowster?
Who learned you to dance,
Babbity-Bowster, brawly?

My minnie learned me to dance,
Babbity-Bowster, Babbity-Bowster.
My minnie learned me to dance,
Babbity-Bowster, brawly.

Who gave you the keys to keep,
Babbity-Bowster, Babbity-Bowster?
Who gave you the keys to keep,
Babbity-Bowster, brawly?

My minnie gave me the keys to keep,
Babbity-Bowster, Babbity-Bowster.
My minnie gave me the keys to keep,
Babbity-Bowster, brawly.

90

Jᴏᴄᴋ plays them rants so lively,
Ballads, reels and jigs,
The foalie flings her muckle legs,
And capers o'er the rigs.

91

JOHNNY, come lend me your fiddle,
If ever you mean to thrive.
O no, I'll not lend my fiddle
To any man alive.

Johnny shall have a blue bonnet,
And Johnny shall go to the fair,
And Johnny shall have a new ribbon,
To tie up his bonny brown hair.

And why should I not love Johnny?
And why should not Johnny love me?
And why should not I love Johnny?
As well as another body?

And here is a leg for a stocking,
And here is a foot for a shoe,
And here is a kiss for his daddy,
And two for his mammie, I trow.

92

KATIE BEARDIE had a cow,
Black and white about the mou,
Wasna that a dainty cow?
Dance Katie Beardie!

Katie Beardie had a hen,
Cackled but and cackled ben,
Wasna that a dainty hen?
  Dance Katie Beardie!

Katie Beardie had a cock,
That could spin, and bake, and rock,
Wasna that a dainty cock?
  Dance Katie Beardie!

Katie Beardie had a grice,
It could skate upon the ice,
Wasna that a dainty grice?
  Dance Katie Beardie!

93

JEAN, Jean, Jean,
The cat's at the cream,
Supping with her forefeet,
And glowering with her een.

94

I'VE found something
That I'll not tell,
All the lads in our town
Clocking in a shell.

All but Robin Robinson
And he's cruppen out,
And he'll have Jean Anderson
Without any doubt.

He kissed her and clapped her,
He's pared all her nails,
He made her a gown
Of peacock tails.

Both coal and candle
Ready to burn,
And they're to be married
The morn's morn.

95

MATTHEW, Mark, Luke, John,
Hold the horse till I leap on;
Hold it siccar, hold it sure,
Till I win o'er the misty moor.

96

BRAW news is come to town,
Braw news is carried;
Braw news is come to town,
Jean Tamson's married.

First she got the frying pan,
Then she got the ladle,
Then she got the young man
Dancing on the table.

97

THERE came a man to our town,
To our town, to our town;
There came a man to our town,
And they called him Aiken Drum.

He played upon a ladle,
A ladle, a ladle;
He played upon a ladle,
And his name was Aiken Drum.

98

WHO saw the Forty-Second?
Who saw them gang awa?
Who saw the Forty-Second
Going to the wapenshaw?
Some of them got chappit tatties,
Some of them got none ava;
Some of them got barley bannocks,
Going to the wapenshaw.

Who saw the Forty-Second?
Who saw them gang awa?
Who saw the Forty-Second
Marching down the Broomielaw?
Some of them had tartan trousers,
Some of them had none ava;
Some of them had green umbrellas,
Marching down the Broomielaw.

99

WILL you buy syboes?
Will you buy leeks?
Will you buy my bonnie lassie
With the red cheeks?

I will not buy your syboes;
I will not buy your leeks;
But I will buy your bonnie lassie
With the red cheeks.

100

O WHAT's the rhyme to porringer?
Ken you the rhyme to porringer?
King James the seventh had a daughter,
And he gave her to an Oranger.

Ken you how she requited him?
Ken you how she requited him?
The lad has into England come,
And taken the crown in spite of him.

The dog, he shall not keep it long,
To flinch we'll make him fain again;
We'll hang him high upon a tree,
And James shall have his ain again.

101

As I went up by yonder hill,
I met my father with good-will;
He had jewels, he had rings,
He had many braw things;
He had a cat with nine tails,
He had a hammer wanting nails.
Up Jack, down Tam,
Blow the bellows, old man!
The old man took a dance,
First to London, then to France.

102

Queen Mary, Queen Mary, my age is sixteen,
My father's a farmer on yonder green,
With plenty of money to dress me full braw,
But no bonnie laddie will take me awa.

Each morning I rose and I looked in the glass,
Says I to myself I'm a handsome young lass;
My hands by my side and I gave a ha! ha!
Yet no bonnie laddie will take me awa.

103

THE crow killed the pussy, O!
The crow killed the pussy, O!
The muckle cat
Sat down and grat
Behind the wee bit housie, O!

The crow killed the pussy, O!
The crow killed the pussy, O!
And aye, aye,
The kitten cried,
"O, who'll bring me a mousie, O?"

104

DANCE to your daddy,
My bonnie laddie,
Dance to your daddy, my bonnie lamb!
And you'll get a fishie
In a little dishie,
You'll get a fishie, when the boat comes hame.

Dance to your daddy,
My bonnie laddie,
Dance to your daddy, my bonnie lamb!
And you'll get a coatie,
And a pair of breekies,
You'll get a whippie and a soople Tam.

105

LAZY ducks, that sit in the coal-nooks,
And will not come out to play,
Leave your supper, and leave your sleep,
Come out and play at hide-and-seek.

106

SINGING GAME

A CHILD stands in the centre of a ring while the others
dance round singing:

> Johnnie Johnson's ta'en a notion,
>> For to go and sail the sea;
> He has left his own true Mollie
>> Weeping by the Greenock Quay.

Here the child in the centre chooses a partner from the
ring. The others whirl round quicker than ever, singing:

> I will buy you beads and earrings,
>> I will buy you diamonds free;
> I will buy you silks and satins,
>> Bonnie, lassie, marry me!

> What care I for beads and earrings!
> What care I for diamonds free!
> What care I for silks and satins,
>> When my love's forsaken me!

107

> O THE dusty miller,
> O the dusty miller,
> Dusty was his coat,
> Dusty was his colour,
> Dusty was the kiss
> I got from the miller!
> O the dusty miller
> With the dusty coat,
> He will spend a shilling
> Ere he win a groat!
> O the dusty miller,
> O the dusty miller!

108

ROUND about the porridge pot,
Fighting for the theevil,
That's the way the money goes.
Pop goes the weasel!

My wee boy's a bonny wee boy,
Your wee boy's a devil;
That's the way the money goes.
Pop goes the weasel!

109

BARNUM and Bayley
Had a canary,
Whistled "The Cock of the North."
It whistled for hours
And frightened the Boers,
And they all fell into the Forth.

B for Boer,
K for Kruger,
J for General French.
The British were up at the top of the hill,
And the Boers were down in the trench.

110

FIRST the heel,
And then the toe,
That's the way
The polka goes.

First the toe,
And then the heel,
That's the way,
To dance a reel.

Quick about,
And then away,
Lightly dance
The glad Strathspey.

Jump a jump,
And jump it big,
That's the way
To dance a jig.

Slowly, smiling,
As in France,
Follow through
The country dance.

And we'll meet Johnnie Cope in the morning!

111

Saw you Eppie Marley, honey,
The wife that sells the barley, honey?
She's lost her pocket and all her money,
With following Jacobite Charlie, honey.

Eppie Marley's turned so fair,
She'll not go out to herd the swine,
But lies in bed till eight or nine,
And won't come down the stairs to dine.

112

When first my Jamie he came to the town,
He had a blue bonnet, a hole in the crown;
But now he has gotten a hat and a feather:
Hey, Jamie lad, cock your beaver,
   Cock your beaver, cock your beaver,
Hey, Jamie lad, cock your beaver!

There's gold behind, there's gold afore,
There's silk in every saddle-bore;
Silver jingling at your bridle,
And grooms to hold your horse when he stands idle.
   So cock your beaver, cock your beaver,
Hey, Jamie lad, cock your beaver!

113

The cock and the hen,
The deer in the den,
Shall drink in the clearest fountain.

The venison rare
Shall be my love's fare,
And I'll follow him over the mountain.

114

As I went by the Luckenbooths
    I saw a lady fair
She had long ear-rings in her ears
    And jewels in her hair.
And when she came to our door,
    She spiered at what was ben,
"Oh, have you seen my lost love,
    With his braw Highland men?"

The smile about her bonnie cheek
    Was sweeter than the bee;
Her voice was like the bird's song
    Upon the birken tree.
But when the minister came out
    Her mare began to prance,
Then rode into the sunset
    Beyond the coast of France.

115

All the night o'er and o'er
And all the night o'er again,
All the night o'er and o'er
The peacock followed the hen.

The hen's a hungry beast,
The cock is hollow within;
But there's nae deceit in a pudding,
A pie's a dainty thing.

All the night o'er and o'er,
And all the night o'er again,
All the night o'er and o'er
The peacock followed the hen.

ALONE in the greenwood must I roam,
　Hollin, green hollin,
A shade of green leaves is my home,
　Birk and green hollin.

Where nought is seen but boundless green,
　Hollin, green hollin;
And spots of far blue sky between,
　Birk and green hollin.

A weary head a pillow finds,
　Hollin, green hollin,
Where leaves fall green in summer winds,
　Birk and green hollin.

Enough for me, enough for me,
　Hollin, green hollin,
To live at large with liberty,
　Birk and green hollin.

117

THE morn's silver Saturday,
The next day's Cockielaw;
We'll come back on Monday,
And give you all a ca.

118

To talk of the weather
It's nothing but folly,
For when it's rain on the hill,
It may be sun in the valley.

119

WEST wind to the bairn,
When going for it's name;
And rain to the corpse,
Carried to its last hame.

A bonny blue sky,
To welcome the bride,
As she goes to the kirk,
With the sun on her side.

120

WIND

ARTHUR of Bower has broken his bands,
And he's come roaring o'er the lands,
The King of Scots and all his power
Cannot turn Arthur of Bower.

121

SNOW

THE men of the East
Are plucking their geese,
And sending their feathers
Here awa, there awa!

122

RAIN, rain, rattle stanes,
Do not rain on me;
But rain on John o' Groats' house,
Far o'er the sea.

THIRTEEN YULE DAYS

THE King sent his lady on the first Yule-day,
A papingoe, aye.
Who learns my carol, and carries it away?

The King sent his lady on the second Yule-day,
Three partridges, a papingoe, aye.
Who learns my carol, and carries it away?

The King sent his lady on the third Yule-day,
Three plovers, three partridges, a papingoe, aye.
Who learns my carol, and carries it away?

The King sent his lady on the fourth Yule-day,
A goose that was grey,
Three plovers, three partridges, a papingoe, aye.
Who learns my carol, and carries it away?

The King sent his lady on the fifth Yule-day,
Three starlings, a goose that was grey,
Three plovers, three partridges, a papingoe, aye,
Who learns my carol, and carries it away?

The King sent his lady on the sixth Yule-day,
Three goldspinks, three starlings, a goose that was grey,
Three plovers, three partridges, a papingoe, aye,
Who learns my carol, and carries it away?

The King sent his lady on the seventh Yule-day,
A bull that was brown,
Three goldspinks, three starlings, a goose that was grey,
Three plovers, three partridges, a papingoe, aye,
Who learns my carol, and carries it away?

The King sent his lady on the eighth Yule-day,
Three ducks a-merry laying, a bull that was brown,
Three goldspinks, three starlings, a goose that was grey,
Three plovers, three partridges, a papingoe, aye.
Who learns my carol, and carries it away?

The King sent his lady on the ninth Yule-day,
Three swans a-merry swimming, three ducks a-merry
        laying,
A bull that was brown,
Three goldspinks, three starlings, a goose that was grey,
Three plovers, three partridges, a papingoe, aye.
Who learns my carol, and carries it away?

The King sent his lady on the tenth Yule-day,
An Arabian baboon,
Three swans a-merry swimming, three ducks a-merry
        laying,
A bull that was brown,
Three goldspinks, three starlings, a goose that was grey,
Three plovers, three partridges, a papingoe, aye.
Who learns my carol, and carries it away?

The King sent his lady on the eleventh Yule-day,
Three hinds a-merry hunting, an Arabian baboon,
Three swans a-merry swimming, three ducks a-merry
    laying,
A bull that was brown,
Three goldspinks, three starlings, a goose that was grey,
Three plovers, three partridges, a papingoe, aye,
Who learns my carol, and carries it away?

The King sent his lady on the twelfth Yule-day,
Three maids a-merry dancing, three hinds a-merry
    hunting,
An Arabian baboon,
Three swans a-merry swimming, three ducks a-merry
    laying,
A bull that was brown,
Three goldspinks, three starlings, a goose that was grey,
Three plovers, three partridges, a papingoe, aye,
Who learns my carol, and carries it away?

The King sent his lady on the thirteenth Yule-day,
Three stalks o merry corn, three maids a-merry dancing,
Three hinds a-merry hunting, an Arabian baboon,
Three swans a-merry swimming, three ducks a-merry
    laying,
A bull that was brown,
Three goldspinks, three starlings, a goose that was grey,
Three plovers, three partridges, a papingoe, aye,
Who learns my carol, and carries it away?

124

Rise up, goodwife, and shake your feathers,
And dinna think that we are beggars;
We are but bairnies come to play,
Rise up and give us our Hogmanay.
Our feet are cold, our shoes thin,
Give us a piece, and let us rin!

125

HOGMANAY

Here come I,
Old Belzebub,
Over my shoulders
I carry my club,
In my hand
A dripping pan,
Amn't I
A jolly old man.

HOGMANAY

HERE comes in Judas,
Judas is my name,
If you put not silver in my bag,
For goodsake mind our wame!
When I went to the castle door,
And tirled at the pin,
They kept the keys of the castle,
And would not let me in.
I have been in the east carse,
I've been in the west carse,
I've been in the Carse of Gowrie
Where the clouds rain all day
Peas and beans,
And the farmers thatch houses
With needles and pins.
I've seen geese going on pattens,
And swine flying in the air
Like peelings of onions!
Our hearts are made of steel,
But our bodies small as wire,—
If you've anything to give us,
Stap it in there.

127

COLLOP Monday,
Pancake Tuesday,
Ash Wednesday,
Bloody Thursday
Long Friday,
Hey for Saturday afternoon;
Hey for Sunday
At twelve o'clock
When all the plum puddings
Jump out of the pot!

128

MONDAY's the fast,
And I'll be daft,
And I'll be dressed in blue,
With red ribbons round my waist,
And sweeties in my mou.

129

Hey-how for Hallowe'en!
All the witches to be seen,
Some black, and some green,
Hey-how for Hallowe'en!

130

This is Hallowe'en,
And the morn's Hallowday;
If you want a true love,
It's time you were away.
Tally on the window-board
Tally on the green,
Tally on the window-board
The morn's Hallowe'en.

131

Haly on a cabbage-stalk,
Haly on a bean,
Haly on a cabbage stalk,
The morn's Hallowe'en!

132

Wee Willie Winkie
Runs through the town,
Up stairs and down stairs,
In his night gown,
Tirling at the window,
Crying through the lock,
"Are all the weans in their bed?
For now it's ten o'clock."

Hey, Willie Winkie,
Are you coming ben?
The cat's singing grey thrums
To the sleeping hen.
The dog's speldered on the floor
And doesn't give a cheep,
But here's a wakeful laddie
That will not fall asleep.

Anything but sleep, you rogue,
Glowering like the moon,
Rattling in an iron jug
With an iron spoon,
Rumbling, tumbling, round about,
Crowing like a cock,
Skirling like a kenna-whit,
Waking sleeping folk.

Hey, Willie Winkie,—
The wean's in the creel!
Wambling off a body's knee
Like a very eel,
Tugging at the cat's ear,
Raveling all her thrums—
Hey Willie Winkie—
See, there he comes!

133

HUSH-A-BA, babby, lie still, lie still;
Your mammie's away to the mill, the mill;
Babby is greeting for want of good keeping,
Hush-a-ba, babby, lie still, lie still.

134

HOOLIE, the bed'll fall!
Who'll fall with it?
Two eyes, two hands,
And two bonnie feet.

Hoolie, the bed'll fall!
Who'll not fall with it?
Wee Robin Redbreast,
Sound asleep.

135

O CAN you sew cushions,
Can you sew sheets,
Can you sing Ba-loo-loo,
When the bairnie greets?

And hee and ba, birdie,
And hee and ba, lamb;
And hee and ba, birdie,
My bonnie wee lamb!

Hee O, wee O,
What shall I do with you?
Black is the life
That I lead with you.

O'er many of you,
Little for to give you;
Hee O, wee O,
What shall I do with you?

I HEARD a cow low, a bonnie cow low,
And a cow low down in yon glen;
Long, long will my young son greet,
Or his mother bid him come ben.

I heard a cow low, a bonny cow low,
And a cow low down in yon fold;
Long, long will my young son greet,
Or his mother shield him from cold.

137

HUSH you, hush you,
Little pet you,
Hush you, hush you,
Dinna fret you,
The Black Douglas
Shall not get you.

138

HUSH-A-BA, birdie, croon, croon,
Hush-a-ba, birdie, croon;
The sheep are gone to the silver wood,
And the cows are gone to the broom, broom.

And it's braw milking the kye, kye,
It's braw milking the kye;
The birds are singing, the bells are ringing,
And the wild deer come galloping by.

Hush-a-ba, birdie, croon, croon,
Hush-a-ba, birdie, croon;
The goats are gone to the mountain high,
And they'll not be home till noon.

WHEN I was a wee thing,
'Bout six or seven year old,
I hadna worth a petticoat,
To keep me frae the cold.

Then I went to Edinburgh,
To bonny burghs town,
And there I coft a petticoat,
A kirtle and a gown.

As I cam hame again,
I thought I would big a kirk,
And all the fowls o the air
Would help me to work.

The heron with her lang neb,
She moupit me the stanes;
The doo, with her rough legs,
She led me them hame.

The gled he was a wily thief,
He rackled up the wall;
The pyat was a curst thief,
She dang down all.

The hare cam hirpling o'er the knowe,
To ring the morning bell;
The hurcheon she cam after,
And said she would dae it hersel.

The heron was the high priest,
The salmon was the clerk,
The howlet read the order,
They held a bonny wark.

140

WHEN I was one, I was in my skin,
When I was twa, I ran awa,
When I was three, I could climb a tree,

When I was four, they dang me o'er,
When I was five, I didna thrive,
When I was six, I got the sticks,
When I was seven, I could count eleven,
When I was eight, I was laid straight,
When I was nine, I could write a line,
When I was ten, I could mend a pen,
When I was eleven, I went to the weaving,
When I was twal, I was Brosy Will.

141

WILLIE, Willie Waddy,
That rides with the king,
Nothing in his pocket,
But a gold ring.

Whiles gold, whiles brass,
Whiles not a thing,
Willie, Willie Waddy,
That rides with the King.

142

TOM TIDDLER'S GROUND

I SET my foot upon Airlie's green,
And Airlie dare not take me;
I cannot get home to stir my porridge,
For Airlie's trying to catch me.

Four-and-twenty Highlandmen
Were riding on a snail,
When up came the hindmost
And trampit on her tail.
O, the snail shot out her wee bit horns,
Just like a hummel cow,
"Hech!" quo the foremost, "we'll all be stickit now!"

Four-and-twenty tailor lads
Were fighting with a slug,
"Hallo, sirs!" said one of them,
"Just hold him by the lug!"
But the beastie from his shell came out,
And shook his fearsome head,
"Run, run, my tailors bold,
Or we will all be dead!"

I went by the mill door,
When out came Miller Reid,
His cap upon his feet,
And his breaks upon his head.
Now, I've sung you all a song,
And I've telt you all a tale,
And it's all big lies
From the head to tail!

144

YOKIE pokie,
Yankie, fun,
How do you like
Your tatties done?

First in brandy,
Then in rum,
That's how I like
My tatties done.

145

MY mother said that I must go
To fetch my daddy's dinner, O.
Chappit tatties, beef and steak,
Two red herrings, and a bawbee cake.

146

BONNIE MAGGIE, braw Maggie,
Bonnie Maggie Bridie, O!
When she got her damask gown,
She lookit like a lady, O!
But when she took it off again,
She was but Maggie Bridie, O!

147

"HIGHLANDMAN, Highlandman,
Where were you born?"

"Up in the Highlands,
Among the green corn."

"What got you there,
But green kail and leeks?"

Laugh at a Highlandman
Wanting his breeks.

148

SHE that goes to the well
With an ill will,
Either the pail breaks
Or the water will spill.

149

Hey dan dilly dow,
How den dan,
Rich was your mother
Gin you were a man.

You'd hunt and you'd hawk,
And keep her in game,
And water your father's horse
In the mill-dam.

Hey dan dilly dow,
How den flowers,
You'll lie in your bed
Till eleven hours.

If at eleven hours
You list to rise
You'll get your dinner
Dight in a new guise.

Laverock's leg,
And titlin's tae,
And all such dainties
My mannie shall hae.

150

I HAVE a wee bit Highlandman,
His name is Sandy Waugh;
He sits upon a puddock-stool,
And sine he sups his broth.

Sing hey, my bonny Highlandman,
My Sandy trig and braw;
Come prinkum prankum, dance with me,
A cock-a-leerie-law.

There's herring in the silver Forth,
And salmon in the Tay,
There's puffins on the old Bass,
And bairns that greet all day.

Sing hey, my bonny Highlandman,
My Sandy trig and braw;
Come prinkum prankum, dance with me,
A cock-a-leerie-law.

151

PADDY on the railway
Picking up stones;
Along came an engine
And broke Paddy's bones.

"O!" said Paddy,
"That's not fair."
"O!" said the engineman,
"You shouldna have been there!"

152

STICKS and stones
Will break my bones,
But names will never hurt me.

When I'm dead,
And in my grave,
You'll be sorry for what you called me!

153

I'M going in a train,
And you're not coming with me;
I've got a lad of my own,
And his name is Kilty Jimmy.

Jimmy wears a kilt,
He wears it in a fashion,
And every time he twirls it round,
You cannot keep from laughing!

154

COLTER'S CANDY

JOHNNIE SCOTT was awful thin,
His bones were sticking through his skin;
Now he's got a double chin,
With eating Colter's candy.

Allabally, allabally bee,
Sitting on your mammie's knee,
Greeting for another bawbee,
To buy some Colter's candy.

155

ME and my grannie,
And a great lot mair
Kickit up a row
Going home from the fair.

By came the watchman,
And cried, "Who goes there?"
"Me and my grannie
And a great lot mair!"

156

HEY, Cocky doo,
How do you do?
Sailing about
In your best of blue.

An alpaca frock,
A green silk shawl,
A white straw bonnet
And a pink parasol.

HAP and row, hap and row,
Hap and row the feetie o't;
I never knew I had a bairn
Until I heard the greetie o't.

The wife put on the wee pan
To boil the bairn's meatie, O,
When down fell a cinder
And burnt all its feetie, O.

Hap and row, hap and row,
Hap and row the feetie o't;
I never knew I had a bairn
Until I heard the greetie o't.

Sandy's mother she came in
As soon as she heard the greetie o't;
She took the cap from off her head
And rowed it round the feetie o't.

Hap and row, hap and row,
Hap and row the feetie o't;
I never knew I had a bairn
Until I heard the greetie o't.

158

As I went up the garden,
I found a little farthing,
I gave it to my mother
To buy a little brother.

My brother was a sailor,
He sailed across the sea,
And all the fish that he could catch
Was one, two, three.

159

As I went by by Humbydrum,
By Humbydrum by dreary,
I met Jehoky poky
Carrying away Jaipeery.

If I had had my tip my tap,
My tip my tap my teerie,
I wouldn't have let Jehoky Poky
Carry away Jaipeery.

O SANDY is a Highland lad,
So brisk and braw and gaudy,
And he's awa to Glasgow town
To steal from me my Peggie.
  Hey lil li lu, hey lil li lan,
  Hey nick and nacketty naggie;
  And he's awa to Glasgow town
  To steal from me my Peggie.

And as he passed the banks and braes,
The banks and braes so bonnie,
'Twas there he spied the little maid—
She said her name was Peggie.
  Hey lil li lu, hey lil li lan,
  Hey nick and nacketty naggie;
  'Twas there he spied a little maid—
  She said her name was Peggie.

"O, come with me, my little maid,
Into the Highlands bonnie;"
"O, no, I winna go with you,
I'll just stay with my mammie!"
  Hey lil li lu, hey lil li lan,
  Hey nick and nacketty naggie;
  "O, no I winna go with you,
  I'll just stay with my mammie!"

O SUCH a hurry-burry!
O such a din!
O such a hurry-burry
Our house is in!

Our hen's eye's out,
Our dog's dead,
Our cat's away from hame
With a sare head.

O such a hurry-burry!
O such a din!
O such a hurry-burry
Our house is in!

162

THE SPIDER

JENNY, good spinner,
Come down to your dinner,
And taste the leg of a roasted frog!
I pray you, good people,
Look over the steeple,
And see the cat play with the dog!

163

O, WHEN I was a wee thing,
Just like a little elf,
Then all the meat that e'er I got
I laid upon the shelf.

But when I got a wifie,
She wouldna bide therein,
Till I got a hurl-barrow braw
To hurl her out and in.

164

I TOOK my foot in my hand,
And hopped o'er to Ireland.

What saw you there?

I saw the grass growing,
The sea flowing,
And the bonnie boats rowing.

165

O MY, you should have seen Colquhoun,
The buttons on his waistcoat were
As big as half a crown.

He got more pay than all the other men,
And the horse that he drove could run
Away with four ton ten.

166

THERE was an old man,
And he lived in the west,
His trade was a cutter
Of broom, green broom.

He had a lazy boy,
And Bob was his name,
And he lay in his bed
Till noon, till noon.

167

THERE'S lots of ways of doing things,
As everyone supposes,
For some turn up their sleeves at work,
And some turn up their noses.

168

"OLD wife, old wife,
Will you go a-shearing?"
"Speak a wee bit louder, sir,
I'm unco dull of hearing."

"Old wife, old wife,
Would you take a kiss?"
"Aye, indeed, I will, sir,
It wouldna be amiss."

169

THE minister in the pulpit,
He couldn't say his prayers,
He laughed and he giggled,
And he fell down the stairs.
The stairs gave a crack,
And he broke his humphy back,
And all the congregation
Went "Quack, quack, quack!"

170

I WOULDNA have a baker, ava, va, va,
I wouldna have a baker ava, va, va,
  For he sits and he cracks,
  And he burns all his baps,
And I wouldna have a baker ava, va, va.

I wouldna have a weaver ava, va, va,
I wouldna have a weaver ava, va, va,
  For he sits and he girns,
  And he ravels all his pirns,
I wouldna have a weaver ava, va, va.

171

WEAVERIE, weaverie wabster,
Gaed up to see the moon,
With all his treadles on his back,
And his sowdie muck abune.

The loom gave a crack,
The weaver gave a grin,
"O, let me down again,
I'll never steal a pin."

"I'll never steal a pin,
I'll never steal a thread,
O let me down again,
I wish that I were dead!"

172

My father died a month ago,
He left me all his riches—
A feather bed and a wooden leg,
And a pair of leather breeches;
A coffee pot without a spout,
A cup without a handle,
A baccy box without a lid,
And half a ha'penny candle.

173

My wheelie goes round,
My wheelie goes round,
And my wheelie she casts the band,
It's not my wheelie that has the wit,
It's my uncanny hand.

174

TAM o the linn came up the gate,
With twenty puddings on a plate,
And each pudding had a pin,
"We'll eat them all," quo Tam o the linn.

Tam o the linn had no breeks to wear,
He bought a sheepskin to make him a pair,
The fleshy side out, the woolly side in,
"It's fine summer clothing," quo Tam o the linn.

Tam o the linn, he had three bairns,
They fell in the fire in each other's arms;
"Oh," quo the last one, "I've got a hot skin."
"It's hotter below," said Tam o the linn.

Tam o the linn went to the moss,
To seek a stable to his horse;
The moss was open, and Tam fell in,
"I've stabled myself," quo Tam o the linn.

175

THERE was a wee wifie rowed up in a blanket,
Nineteen times as high as the moon;
And what she did there I cannot declare,
For in her oxter she bore the sun.

"Wee wifie, wee wifie, wee wifie," quo I,
"What are you doing up there so high?"
"I'm blowing the cold clouds out of the sky."
"Well done, well done, wee wifie," quo I.

176

I'M not, says she,
So braw, says she,
Nor yet, says she,
So big, says she,
But I'll go, says she,
To Perth, says she,
And get, says she,
A man, says she,
And then, says she,
I'll be, says she,
As good, says she,
As you, says she.

177

"SANDY," quo he, "lend me your mill!"
"Sandy," quo he, "lend me your mill!"
"Sandy," quo he, "lend me your mill!"
"Lend you my mill?" quo Sandy.

Sandy lent the man his mill,
And the man got a loan of Sandy's mill,
And the mill that was lent was Sandy's mill,
And the mill belonged to Sandy.

178

COME a riddle, come a riddle,
Come a rot-tot-tot;
A wee, wee man, in a red, red coat,
A staff in his hand and a bone in his throat;
Come a riddle, come a riddle,
Come a rot-tot-tot.

A Cherry

179

THIS is the tree
That never grew,
This is the bird,
That never flew.
This is the bell
That never rang.
And this is the fish
That never swam.

The Arms of Glasgow

180

THERE'S a wee, wee house,
And it's full of meat;
But neither door nor window
Will let you in to eat.

An egg

181

A HA'PENNY here, and a ha'penny there,
Fourpence ha'penny, and a ha'penny more,
A ha'penny wet, and a ha'penny dry,
Fourpence ha'penny, and a ha'penny forby—
How much is that?

A shilling

182

I saw a peacock with a fiery tail
I saw a blazing comet pour down hail
I saw a cloud wrapt with ivy round
I saw an oak creeping on the ground
I saw an ant swallow up a whale,
I saw the sea brimful of ale
I saw a Venice glass fifteen feet deep
I saw a well full of men's tears that weep
I saw wet eyes all of a flaming fire
I saw a horse bigger than the moon and higher
I saw the sun even at midnight—
I saw the man who saw this dreadful sight.

183

John Smith's a very good man,
Teaches scholars now and then,
And when he's done he takes a dance,
Up to London, down to France.

184

THE FISHERMEN'S SONG

O BLITHELY shines the bonnie sun
Upon the Isle of May,
And blithely rolls the morning tide
Into St. Andrew's bay.

When haddocks leave the Firth of Forth,
And mussels leave the shore,
When oysters climb up Berwick Law,
We'll go to sea no more,
No more,
We'll go to sea no more.

185

HAILY Paily,
Sits on the sands,
Combs her hair
With her lily-white hands.

186

FOUR-AND-TWENTY mermaids,
Who left the port of Leith,
To tempt the fine old hermit,
Who dwelt upon Inchkeith.

No boat, nor waft, nor crayer,
Nor craft had they, nor oars nor sails;
Their lily hands were oars enough,
Their tillers were their tails.

187

O, PEARLIN Jean!
O, Pearlin Jean!
She haunts the house,
She haunts the green,
And glowers on me
With her wild-cat een.

188

THE GHOST'S SONG

WAE's me, wae's me!
The acorn's no yet
Fallen frae the tree,
That's to grow the wood,
That's to mak the cradle,
That's to rock the bairn,
That's to grow a man,
That's to lay me.

I HAD three little sisters across the sea,
   Peerie, weerie, winkum, do, re, me;
What handsome presents they all sent me,
   Pinkum, quartum, Paradise lost them,
    Peerie, weerie, winkum, do, re, me.

The first was a chicken without a bone,
   Peerie, weerie, winkum, do, re, me;
The second was a cherry without a stone,
   Pinkum, quartum, Paradise lost them,
    Peerie, weerie, winkum, do, re, me.

The third was a blanket without a thread,
   Peerie, weerie, winkum, do, re, me;
The fourth was a book that couldn't be read,
   Pinkum, quartum, Paradise lost them,
    Peerie, weerie, winkum, do, re, me.

How could there be a chicken without a bone?
   Peerie, weerie, winkum, do, re, me;
How could there be a cherry without a stone?
   Pinkum, quartum, Paradise lost them,
    Peerie, weerie, winkum, do, re, me.

How could there be a blanket without a thread?
   Peerie, weerie, winkum, do, re, me;
How could there be a book that couldn't be read?
   Pinkum, quartum, Paradise lost them,
    Peerie, weerie, winkum, do, re, me.

The chicken in the egg without a bone,
  Peerie, weerie, winkum, do, re, me;
The cherry in the blossom without a stone,
  Pinkum, quartum, Paradise lost them,
    Peerie, weerie, winkum, do, re, me.

The blanket in the fleece without a thread,
  Peerie, weerie, winkum, do, re, me;
The book in the press that couldn't be read,
  Pinkum, quartum, Paradise lost them,
    Peerie, weerie, winkum, do, re, me.

190

STRUTHILL WELL

THREE white stones,
And three black pins,
Three yellow gowans
Off the green,

Into the well,
With a one, two, three,
And a fortune, a fortune,
Come to me.

BONNY SAINT JOHN

WHERE have you been,
My bonny Saint John?
You've biden sae lang,
You've biden sae lang.

Where have you been,
My bonny Saint John?
You've biden sae lang,
You've biden sae lang.

Up on yon hill,
And down in yon glen,
And I couldna win hame,
And I couldna win hame.

Now, what will you give me
Unto my supper,
Now, when I've come hame,
Now, when I've come hame?

A clean dish for you,
And a clean spoon,
For biding sae lang,
For biding sae lang.

A clean dish for you,
And a clean spoon,
For biding sae lang,
For biding sae lang.

192

"Buy me a milking pail,
　　Mother, mother,"
"Betsy's gone a-milking,
　　Beautiful daughter."

"Sell my father's feather bed,
　　Mother, mother."
"Where will your father lie,
　　Beautiful daughter?"

"Put him in the boy's bed,
　　Mother, mother."
"Where will the boy's lie,
　　Beautiful daughter?"

"Put them in the pig's sty,
　　Mother, mother,"
"Where will the pigs lie,
　　Beautiful daughter?"

"Put them in the salting tub,
　　Mother, mother."

193

THERE dwelt a Puddy in a well,
  Cuddy alane, cuddy alane;
There dwelt a Puddy in a well,
  Cuddy alane and I.
There was a Puddy in a well,
And a mousie in a mill;
  Kickmaleerie, cowden down,
  Cuddy alane and I.
Puddy he'd a wooing ride,
  Cuddy alane, cuddy alane;
Puddy he'd a wooing ride,
  Cuddy alane and I.
Puddy he'd a wooing ride,
Sword and pistol by his side;
  Kickmaleerie, cowden down,
  Cuddie alane and I.
Puddy came to the mouse's wonne,
  Cuddy alane, cuddy alane;
Puddy came to the mouse's wonne,
  Cuddy alane and I.

Puddy came to the mouse's wonne,
"Mistress Mouse are you within?"
  Kickmaleerie, cowden down,
  Cuddy alane and I.
"Aye, kind sir, I am within,"
  Cuddy alane, cuddy alane;
"Aye, kind sir, I am within,"
  Cuddy alane and I.
"Aye, kind sir, I am within,
Softly do I sit and spin;"
  Kickmaleerie, cowden down,
  Cuddy alane and I.
"Madam, I am come to woo,"
  Cuddy alane, cuddy alane;
"Madam, I am come to woo,"
  Cuddy alane and I.
"Madam, I am come to woo,
Marriage I maun have of you;"
  Kickmaleerie, cowden down,
  Cuddy alane and I.
"Marriage I will grant you nane,"
  Cuddy alane, cuddy alane;
"Marriage I will grant you nane,"
  Cuddy alane and I.
"Marriage I will grant you nane,
Till Uncle Rottan he comes hame;"
  Kickmaleerie, cowden down,
  Cuddy alane and I.
Uncle Rottan's now come hame,
  Cuddy alane, cuddy alane;
Uncle Rottan's now come hame,
  Cuddy alane and I;

Uncle Rottan's now come hame,
"Fy, gar busk the bride alang!"
   Kickmaleerie, cowden down,
   Cuddy alane and I.
Lord Rottan sat at the head of the table,
   Cuddy alane, cuddy alane;
Lord Rottan sat at the head of the table,
   Cuddy alane and I.
Lord Rottan sat at the head of the table,
For that he was both stout and able;
   Kickmaleerie, cowden down,
   Cuddy alane and I.
Who is it that sits next the wall?
   Cuddy alane, cuddy alane;
Who is it that sits next the wall?
   Cuddy alane and I.
Who is it that sits next the wall,
But Lady Mouse both jimp and small;
   Kickmaleerie, cowden down,
   Cuddy alane and I.
Who is it that sits next the bride?
   Cuddy alane, cuddy alane;
Who is it that sits next the bride?
   Cuddy alane and I.
Who is it that sits next the bride,
But the sola Puddy with the yellow side;
   Kickmaleerie, cowden down,
   Cuddy alane and I.
Syne came the Duck but, and the Drake,
   Cuddy alane, cuddy alane;
Syne came the Duck but, and the Drake,
   Cuddy alane and I.

Syne came the Duck but, and the Drake;
The Duck took the Puddy and gart him squeak;
   Kickmaleerie, cowden down,
   Cuddy alane and I.

Then came in the good grey Cat,
   Cuddy alane, cuddy alane;
Then came in the good grey Cat,
   Cuddy alane and I.
Then came in the good grey Cat,
With all the kittlings at her back;
   Kickmaleerie, cowden down,
   Cuddy alane and I.

The Puddy he swam down the brook,
   Cuddy alane, cuddy alane;
The Puddy he swam down the brook,
   Cuddy alane and I.
The Puddy he swam down the brook;
The Drake he catched him in his fluke;
   Kickmaleerie, cowden down,
   Cuddy alane and I.

The Cat he pulled Lord Rottan down,
   Cuddy alane, cuddy alane;
The Cat he pulled Lord Rottan down
   Cuddy alane and I.
The Cat he pulled Lord Rottan down,
The kittlings they did claw his crown;
   Kickmaleerie, cowden down,
   Cuddy alane and I.

But Lady Mouse, both jimp and small,
   Cuddy alane, cuddy alane;
But Lady Mouse, both jimp and small,
   Cuddy alane and I.

But Lady Mouse, both jimp and small,
Crept into a hole beneath the wall;
"Squeak!" quo she, "I'm well awa!"
   Kickmaleerie, cowden down,
   Cuddy alane and I.

194

ROBIN REDBREAST'S TESTAMENT

"GOOD day now, bonnie Robin,
How lang have you been here?"
"I've been bird about this bush
This mair than twenty year.
Chorus: Teetle ell ell, teetle ell ell,
         Teetle ell ell, teetle ell ell,
         Tee tee tee tee, tee tee tee,
         Tee tee tee tee, teetle eldie.

"But now I am the sickest bird
That ever sat on brier;
And I would mak my testament,
Goodman, if you would hear.

"Gar tak this bonnie neb of mine,
That picks upon the corn,
And gie't to the Duke of Hamilton,
To be a hunting-horn.

"Gar tak they bonnie feathers of mine,
The feathers of my neb;
And give to the Lady of Hamilton,
To fill a feather-bed.

"Gar tak this good right leg of mine,
And mend the brig of Tay;
'Twill be a post and pillar good,
'Twill neither bow nor gae.

"And tak this other leg of mine,
And mend the brig of Weir;
'Twill be a post and pillar good,
It'll neither bow nor steer.

"Gar tak they bonny feathers of mine,
The feathers of my tail;
And give to the lads of Hamilton,
To be a barn flail.

"And tak they bonny feathers of mine,
The feathers of my breast;
And give to any bonny lad
That'll bring to me a priest."

Now in there came my Lady Wren,
With many a sigh and groan;
"O, what care I for all the lads,
Gin my wee lad be gone?"

Then Robin turned him round about,
E'en like a little king;
"Go, pack you out at my chamber-door,
You little cutty-quean."

Robin made his testament
Upon a coll of hay;
And by came a greedy gled,
And snapped him all away.

195

THE cattie sat in the kiln-ring,
  Spinning, spinning;
And by cam a little wee mousie,
  Running, running.

"Oh, what's that you're spinning, my loesome,
  Loesome lady?"
"I'm spinning a sark to my young son,"
  Said she, said she.

"Well mot he brook it, my loesome,
  Loesome lady."
"If he dinna brook it well, he may brook it ill,"
  Said she, said she.

I soopit my house, my loesome,
 Loesome lady."
"'Twas a sign ye didna sit among dirt, then,"
 Said she, said she.

"I found twelve pennies, my winsome,
 Winsome lady."
"'Twas a sign ye werena sillerless,"
 Said she, said she.

"I gaed to the market, my loesome,
 Loesome lady."
"'Twas a sign ye didna sit at hame, then,"
 Said she, said she.

"I coft a sheepie's head, my winsome,
 Winsome lady."
"'Twas a sign ye werena kitchenless,"
 Said she, said she.

"I put it in my pottie to boil, my loesome,
 Loesome lady."
"'Twas a sign ye didna eat it raw,"
 Said she, said she.

"I put it in my winnock to cool, my winsome,
 Winsome lady."
"'Twas a sign ye didna burn your chafts, then,"
 Said she, said she.

"By cam a cattie, and ate it all up, my loesome,
 Loesome lady."
"And so will I you—worry, worry—guash, guash."
 Said she, said she.

144

THE STRANGE VISITOR

A WIFE was sitting at her reel ae nicht;
And aye she sat, and aye she reeled, and aye she wished
for company.

In cam a pair o braid, braid soles, and sat down at the
fireside;
And aye she sat, and aye she reeled, and aye she wished
for company.

In cam a pair o sma, sma legs, and sat down on the
braid, braid soles;
And aye she sat, and aye she reeled, and aye she wished
for company.

In cam a pair o sma, sma thees, and sat down on the
sma, sma legs;
And aye she sat, and aye she reeled, and aye she wished
for company.

In cam a pair o muckle, muckle hips, and sat down on
  the sma, sma thees;
And aye she sat, and aye she reeled, and aye she wished
  for company.

In cam a sma, sma waist, and sat down on the muckle,
  muckle hips;
And aye she sat, and aye she reeled, and aye she wished
  for company.

In cam a pair o braid, braid shouthers, and sat down on
  the sma, sma waist;
And aye she sat, and aye she reeled, and aye she wished
  for company.

In cam a pair o sma, sma arms, and sat down on the
  braid, braid shouthers;
And aye she sat, and aye she reeled, and aye she wished
  for company.

In cam a pair o muckle, muckle hands, and sat down on
  the sma, sma arms;
And aye she sat, and aye she reeled, and aye she wished
  for company.

In cam a sma, sma neck, and sat down on the braid,
  braid shouthers;
And aye she sat, and aye she reeled, and aye she wished
  for company.

In cam a great big head, and sat down on the sma, sma
  neck.

"What way hae ye sic braid, braid feet?" quo the wife.
"Muckle ganging, muckle ganging."
"What way hae ye sic sma, sma legs?"
"*Aih-h-h!*—late—and *wee-e-e*—moul."

"What way hae ye sic muckle, muckle knees?"
"Muckle praying, muckle praying."
"What way hae ye sic sma, sma thees?"
"*Aih-h-h!*—late—and *wee-e-e*—moul."
"What way hae ye sic big, big hips?"
"Muckle sitting, muckle sitting."
"What way hae ye sic a sma, sma waist?"
Aih-h-h!—late—and *wee-e-e* moul."
"What way hae ye sic braid, braid shouthers?"
"Wi carrying broom, wi carrying broom."
"What way hae ye sic sma, sma arms?"
"*Aih-h-h*—late—and *wee-e-e*—moul."
"What way hae ye sic muckle, muckle hands?"
"Threshing wi an iron flail, threshing wi an iron flail."
"What way hae ye sic a sma, sma neck?"
"*Aih-h-h*—late—and *wee-e-e*—moul."
"What way hae ye sic a muckle, muckle head?"
"Muckle wit, muckle wit."
"What do ye come for?"
For you!"

197

"O, WHERE are you going?"
Quo the false knight upon the road;
"I'm going to the school."
Quo the wee boy, and still he stood.

"What is that upon your back?"
Quo the false knight upon the road;
"Ah well, it is my books,"
Quo the wee boy, and still he stood.

"What's that you've under your arm?"
Quo the false knight upon the road.
"Ah well, it is my peat,"
Quo the wee boy, and still he stood.

"Who's acht they sheep?"
Quo the false knight upon the road,
"They're mine and my mother's,"
Quo the wee boy, and still he stood.

"How many of them are mine?"
Quo the false knight upon the road.
"All they that have blue tails,"
Quo the wee boy, and still he stood.

"I wish you were on yon tree,"
Quo the false knight upon the road,
"And a good ladder under me,"
Quo the wee boy, and still he stood.

"And the ladder for to break,"
Quo the false knight upon the road.
"And for you to fall down,"
Quo the wee boy, and still he stood.

"I wish you were in yon sea,"
Quo the false knight upon the road;
"And a good coble under me,"
Quo the wee boy, and still he stood.

"And the coble for to break,"
Quo the false knight upon the road.
"And you to be drowned,"
Quo the wee boy, and still he stood.

THE WEE, WEE MAN

As I was walking all alane,
Atween a water and a wa,
O there I met a wee, wee man,
And he was the least I ever saw.

His legs were scarce a shathmont lang,
And thick and thimber was his thigh;
Atween his brows there was a span,
And atween his shouthers there was three.

And he took up a muckle stane,
And flung it as far as I could see;
Though I had been the Wallace wight,
I couldna lift it to my knee.

"O, wee, wee man, but thou be strang!
O, tell me where thy dwelling be!"
"My dwelling's down at yon bonny bower,
O, will you gang with me and see?"

On we lap, and away we rade,
Till we came to yon bonny green;
We lighted down to bait our horse,
And out there cam a lady fine.

Four-and-twenty at her back,
And they were all clad out in green;
Though the King of Scotland had been there
The worst of them might have been his queen.

And on we lap, and away we rade,
Till we cam to yon bonny hall,
Where the roof was of the beaten gold,
And the floor was of the crystal all.

And there were harpings loud and sweet,
And ladies dancing jimp and small;
But in the twinkling of an eye,
My wee, wee man was clean awa.

199

THE WEE CROODIN DOO

"Where have you been all the day,
My bonny wee crooding doo?"
"O, I have been at my stepmother's house;
Mak my bed, mammie, noo, noo, noo!
Mak my bed, mammie noo!"

"Where did you get your dinner,
My bonny wee crooding doo?"
"I got in my stepmother's;
Mak my bed, mammie, noo, noo, noo!
Mak my bed, mammie, noo!"

"What did she give you to your dinner,
My bonny wee crooding doo?"
"She gave me a wee four-footed fish;
Mak my bed, mammie, noo, noo, noo!
Mak my bed, mammie, noo!"

"Where got she the four-footed fish,
My bonny wee crooding doo?"
"She got it down in yon well-strand;
Mak my bed, mammie, noo, noo, noo!
Mak my bed, mammie, noo!"

"What did she dae with the banes o't,
My bonny wee crooding doo?"
"She gave them to the wee dog;
Mak my bed, mammie, noo, noo, noo!
Mak my bed, mammie, noo!"

"O what becam of the wee dog,
My bonny wee crooding doo?"
"O, it shot out its feet and died!
O, mak my bed, mammie, noo, noo, noo!
O mak my bed, mammie, noo!"

200

QUEEN MARY'S MEN

THIS is good New Year's Even-night,
  We are all Queen Mary's men;
And we've come here to claim our right,
  And that's before our Lady.

Old man, gae to your ale-in-vat,
  We are all Queen Mary's men;
And hand us here twa pints of that!
  And that's before our Lady.

Goodwife, gae to your pork-ham,
  We are all Queen Mary's men;
And cut it large and cut it round,
Be sure you cut not your big thumb!
  And that's before our Lady.

Here's to the one with the yellow hair,
    We are all Queen Mary's men;
She's in the house and we maun have her,
    And that's before our Lady.

I wish your kine may all well thrive,
    We are all Queen Mary's men;
And every one a good calf,
    And that's before our Lady.

I wish your mares well in their boal,
    We are all Queen Mary's men;
And every one a stag foal,
    And that's before our Lady.

I wish your hens may all well thrive,
    We are all Queen Mary's men;
And every one lay three times five,
    And that's before our Lady.

I wish your geese well frae the hill,
    We are all Queen Mary's men;
And every one twelve at her heel,
    And that's before our Lady.

Orkney

INDEX OF FIRST LINES

153

156

THE END

A book of Scottish

DATE DUE

FEB 22 '78			